Written Calculation
Division 2
Answers

Schofield&Sims

Introduction for parents and teachers

This book provides correct answers to all the questions in the Pupil Book **Written Calculation: Division 2** (ISBN 978 07217 1271 0), including those contained in each **Check-up test** and **Final test**.

Which pupils will benefit most from Written Calculation: Division 2?

Written Calculation covers division in two books: pupils should work through both books consecutively to ensure that all the necessary steps are covered. **Division 2** is for pupils who already understand the value of digits in numbers and have worked through **Division 1**. They are able to identify the units digit in a four-digit number such as 5468. They also know the values of the other digits, including tens, hundreds and thousands. Pupils should also be experienced with multiplying and dividing small numbers (for example, 4 × 8, 32 ÷ 4). Pupils who know by heart all their times tables and related division facts will find written division easier than those who have to work them out. For this reason, pupils who have not yet memorised their tables may find it useful temporarily to refer to a multiplication square – downloadable from the Schofield & Sims website – from which they can derive the related division facts. This will allow them to focus on the procedures of the written method. Once the pupils are familiar with the facts, they will no longer need the multiplication square. Where the subtractions are easy, not all carrying figures are shown as pupils are expected to be able to do these in their head.

How should the Pupil Book be used?

Pupils should work consecutively through all 18 'steps' if they are to become fully proficient in the most important stages of the learning process. At the end of each step are **Problem Solving** questions. Pupils record their workings onto the grids provided and also write their answers in the book. Make sure that each pupil completes the **self-evaluation** rating at the end of each step by ticking 'Easy', 'OK' or 'Difficult'. Review each pupil's rating against his or her score for that step, and give support to pupils who are struggling. The final steps in the book extend more able pupils and take them beyond the statutory aspects of written division, requiring them to work with larger numbers and decimals, for example. **Check-up tests** and a **Final test** help you to monitor progress, and this book of **Answers** makes marking simple and quick. Use the **conversion chart** at the end of each test to quickly convert the pupil's score to a percentage that can be recorded and used to measure progress.

Please note: Pupils will require additional squared paper to help them complete some of the pages in the Pupil Book.

The separate **Written Calculation: Teacher's Guide** (ISBN 978 07217 1278 9) contains full teaching notes and assessment resources. The **Teacher's Resource Book** (ISBN 978 07217 1300 7) contains photocopiable resources. Both cover the whole series and provide the teacher with valuable guidance and resources to support the teaching of written calculation. For free downloads and for further details on all the other **Written Calculation** books, visit **www.schofieldandsims.co.uk**

Published by Schofield & Sims Ltd, Dogley Mill, Fenay Bridge, Huddersfield HD8 0NQ, UK Tel 01484 607080 www.schofieldandsims.co.uk

First published in 2015. Copyright © Schofield & Sims Ltd, 2015.

Authors: **Hilary Koll and Steve Mills**

Hilary Koll and Steve Mills have asserted their moral rights under the Copyright, Designs and Patents Act, 1988, to be identified as the authors of this work.

British Library Cataloguing in Publication Data

A catalogue record for this book is available from the British Library.

Commissioned by **Carolyn Richardson Publishing Services** (www.publiserve.co.uk)

Design by **Ledgard Jepson Ltd**

Cover illustration by **Joe Hance** (joehance.co.uk)

Printed in the UK by **Wyndeham Gait Ltd, Grimsby, Lincolnshire**

ISBN 978 07217 1277 2

Contents

Step 1: Three-digit ÷ one-digit short division revision

In **Division 1** you learnt how to divide by one-digit numbers such as $945 \div 7$ (short division). In this book you will learn how to do **long division** where you divide by two-digit numbers such as $945 \div 70$. First we will revise short division.

$945 \div 7 = ?$

What to do (a reminder)

1 As usual, work from the left and divide each digit by the divisor. Write your answer on top of the line. Start with the hundreds digit of the large number. Here it is 9. Divide this digit by the divisor, 7. Ask: *How many 7s in 9? 9 ÷ 7 = 1 remainder 2.* So write the 1 above the line in the hundreds column and carry the 2 next to the tens digit of the large number.

2 Then look at the tens. Instead of 4 tens we now have 24 tens. Divide by the divisor, 7. Ask: *How many 7s in 24? 24 ÷ 7 = 3 r3.* Write the 3 above the line in the tens column and carry the remaining 3 to the units column.

3 Now look at the units. Instead of 5 units we now have 35 units. Divide this digit by the divisor, 7. Ask: *How many 7s in 35? 35 ÷ 7 = 5.* Write the answer 5 above the line in the units column.

$945 \div 7 = 135$

Now you try

1 $5 \overline{)9\ ^46\ ^15}$ = 193

2 $4 \overline{)7\ ^34\ ^24}$ = 186

3 $8 \overline{)3\ ^36\ ^48}$ = 046

4 $6 \overline{)9\ ^31\ ^18}$ = 153

5 $3 \overline{)9\ 8\ ^24}$ = 328

6 $6 \overline{)7\ ^15\ ^36}$ = 126

More practice

Set out these questions yourself to answer them.

7 726 ÷ 3 = ?

	H	T	U
		2	4	2

3) 7 ^{1}2 6

8 378 ÷ 9 = ?

	H	T	U
		0	4	2

9) 3 ^{3}7 ^{1}8

9 836 ÷ 4 = ?

	H	T	U
		2	0	9

4) 8 3 ^{3}6

10 584 ÷ 8 = ?

	H	T	U
		0	7	3

8) 5 ^{5}8 ^{2}4

Problem solving

11 The area of a rectangle is found by multiplying the length by the width. If a rectangle has an area of 342cm^2 and a width of 9cm, what is its length?

      0 3 8
9) 3 ^{3}4 ^{7}2   38cm
——————

12 To convert measurements in feet into yards, divide by three. How many yards is 456 feet?

      1 5 2
3) 4 ^{1}5 6   152 yards
——————

13 If one-seventh of the 196 countries of the world speak French, how many countries speak French?

      0 2 8
7) 1 ^{1}9 ^{5}6   28
——————

| **How did I find Step 1?** | ☐ Easy | ☐ OK | ☐ Difficult |

Step 2: Five-digit ÷ one-digit short division with remainders revision

These questions revise short division of larger numbers and giving answers with remainders.

What to do

$83229 \div 6 = ?$

1 As usual, work from the left and divide each digit by the divisor. For the first digit ask: *How many 6s in 8?* $8 \div 6 = 1$ r2. Write the 1 above and carry the 2.

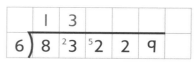

2 Then look at the next digit. Instead of 3 we now have 23. Ask: *How many 6s in 23?* $23 \div 6 = 3$ r5. Write the 3 above and carry the 5.

3 Look at the next digit. Instead of 2 we now have 52. $52 \div 6 = 8$ r4. Write 8 above and carry the 4.

4 For the next digit, we now have 42. $42 \div 6 = 7$. Write the answer 7 above.

5 Finally divide 9 by 6, which is 1 r3. Write this above the line to complete the answer.

$83229 \div 6 = 13871$ remainder 3

Now you try

1

2
```
      1 9 2 0 5 r2
  3)5 ²7 6 1 ¹7
```

3

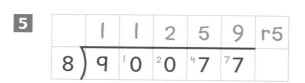

4

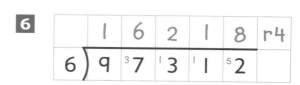

5
```
      1 1 2 5 9 r5
  8)9 ¹0 ²0 ⁴7 ⁷7
```

6
```
      1 6 2 1 8 r4
  6)9 ³7 ¹3 ¹1 ⁵2
```

More practice

Set out these questions yourself to answer them, including drawing the horizontal and vertical lines.

7 44 444 ÷ 5 = ?   _8888 r4_

	TTh	Th	H	T	U	
	0	8	8	8	8	r4
5)	4	⁴4	⁴4	⁴4	⁴4	

8 44 444 ÷ 6 = ?   _7407 r2_

	TTh	Th	H	T	U	
	0	7	4	0	7	r2
6)	4	⁴4	²4	4	⁴4	

9 44 444 ÷ 7 = ?   _6349 r1_

	TTh	Th	H	T	U	
	0	6	3	4	9	r1
7)	4	⁴4	²4	³4	⁶4	

10 44 444 ÷ 8 = ?   _5555 r4_

	TTh	Th	H	T	U	
	0	5	5	5	5	r4
8)	4	⁴4	⁴4	⁴4	⁴4	

Problem solving

11 Choose a single digit to repeat to make a five-digit number, such as 55 555.
Divide the number by 9 and write the remainder. Do this as many times as you can.
What remainders can you get? Use spare squared paper for working.

> 99 999 has no remainder, 88 888 has a remainder of 4,
> 77 777 has a remainder of 8, 66 666 has a remainder of 3,
> 55 555 has a remainder of 7, 44 444 has a remainder of 2,
> 33 333 has a remainder of 6, 22 222 has a remainder of 1,
> 11 111 has a remainder of 5.

How did I find Step 2?   ☐ Easy   ☐ OK   ☐ Difficult

Step 3: Two-digit ÷ one-digit long division

Now we are starting long division, remember **DMS: Divide, Multiply, Subtract**. You will do this over and over as part of this method. Long division is a method which is useful for dividing by divisors greater than 9. We will start by learning the method with smaller divisors.

What to do

$94 \div 4 = ?$

1 As with short division start by dividing the tens digit by the divisor, 4. Ask: *How many 4s in 9?* $9 \div 4 = 2$ r1. So write the answer 2 above the line. **Don't carry** the 1 this time!

2 Instead, point to the digit you've just written (2) and **multiply** it by the divisor. $2 \times 4 = 8$. Write the answer under the tens digit. Draw a line under it and **subtract** it from the digit above. $9 - 8 = 1$. (Note that this 1 is the number you would have carried.)

3 Now bring the units digit down next to the 1 you have just written to give 14. Divide this number by the divisor, 4. Ask: *How many 4s in 14?* Write the answer 3 above the line but **don't carry** the 2.

4 Instead point to the digit you've just written (3) and **multiply** it by the divisor. $3 \times 4 = 12$. Write the answer, 12, under the 14. Draw a line under it and **subtract** it. $14 - 12 = 2$. (This is the number you would have carried.) As there are no other digits to divide this is the remainder, so write r2 at the top next to 23 to give the answer 23 r2.

Now you try

1

```
      2  6  r1
  3)  7  9
  -   6
      1  9
  -   1  8
         1
```

2

```
      1  4  r2
  4)  5  8
  -   4
      1  8
  -   1  6
         2
```

3

```
      2  9  r2
  3)  8  9
  -   6
      2  9
  -   2  7
         2
```

More practice

4

```
        1   6  r3
  6 ) 9   9
   -  6
        3   9
   -    3   6
            3
```

5

```
        2   4  r1
  4 ) 9   7
   -  8
        1   7
   -    1   6
            1
```

6

```
        4   8  r1
  2 ) 9   7
   -  8
        1   7
   -    1   6
            1
```

Problem solving

7 Spot the error in this calculation and explain what the mistake is. Give the correct answer.

```
          2   4  r4
  3 ) 7   6
   -  6
        1   6
   -    1   2
            4
```

Error: Rather than 4 x 3 = 12 r4, it should
_____
have been 5 x 3 = 15 r1.
_____
Correct answer: 25 r1
_____

Use spare squared paper for working and the long division method to solve these problems.

8 Find the answer to 95 ÷ 7.   ___13 r4___

9 Which of these questions have an answer with a remainder of 2?

98 ÷ 4   79 ÷ 3   85 ÷ 4   83 ÷ 3   ___98 ÷ 4 and 83 ÷ 3___

10 Find the difference between one-third of 87 and one-quarter of 76.   ___10___

How did I find Step 3?   ☐ Easy   ☐ OK   ☐ Difficult

Step 4: Three-digit ÷ one-digit long division

Remember **DMS: Divide, Multiply, Subtract**. After each subtraction bring down the next digit.

$857 \div 3 = ?$

What to do

1 Divide the hundreds digit by the divisor, 3. Ask: *How many 3s in 8?* $8 \div 3 = 2$ r2. Write 2 above the hundreds digit.

	H	T	U
	2		
3)	8	5	7
−	6		
	2		

2 Point to the digit just written (2) and **multiply** it by the divisor. $2 \times 3 = 6$. Put the answer 6 below the hundreds digit. Draw a line under it and **subtract** it. $8 - 6 = 2$

3 Now bring the tens digit down next to the 2 to give 25. Divide this number by the divisor, 3. Ask: *How many 3s in 25?* Write the whole number part of the answer, 8.

4 Point to the digit just written (8) and **multiply** it by the divisor. $8 \times 3 = 24$. Write the answer, 24, under the 25. Draw a line under it and **subtract** it. $25 - 24 = 1$

		2	8	5	r2
	3)	8	5	7	
	−	6			
		2	5		
	−	2	4		
			1	7	
		−	1	5	
				2	

5 Now bring the units digit down next to the 1 to give 17. Ask: *How many 3s in 17?* Write 5 above and multiply it by the divisor 3 to give 15. Subtract 15 from 17.

6 As there are no other digits this is the remainder, so write r2 at the top next to 285 to give the answer 285 r2.

Now you try

1

		2	6	5	r2
	3)	7	9	7	
	−	6			
		1	9		
	−	1	8		
			1	7	
		−	1	5	
				2	

2

		1	7	3	r1
	4)	6	9	3	
	−	4			
		2	9		
	−	2	8		
			1	3	
		−	1	2	
				1	

More practice

3

```
        1   3   7  r2
   5 ) 6   8   7
   -   5
       1   8
   -   1   5
           3   7
       -   3   5
               2
```

4

```
        1   3   9  r5
   7 ) 9   7   8
   -   7
       2   7
   -   2   1
           6   8
       -   6   3
               5
```

Problem solving

5 Spot the error in this calculation and explain what the mistake is. Give the correct answer.

Error: The subtraction of 29 – 24 is wrong.

The answer to this should be 5, and

therefore the number will be 57.

Correct answer: 149 r3

```
        1   4   6  r1
   6 ) 8   9   7
   -   6
       2   9
   -   2   4
           3   7
       -   3   6
               1
```

Use spare squared paper for working and the long division method to solve these problems.

6 Find what number when multiplied by 4 gives the answer 676.

169

7 How many teams of three could be made with 588 children?

196

How did I find Step 4?   ☐ Easy   ☐ OK   ☐ Difficult

Step 5: Four-digit ÷ one-digit long division

Remember: **DMS (Divide, Multiply, Subtract)** *then bring down the next digit.*
In this step also remember that anything multiplied by zero is zero!

What to do

$2972 \div 4 = ?$

	Th	H	T	U	
		0	7	4	3
4)	2	9	7	2	
−	0				
	2	9			
−	2	8			
		1	7		
	−	1	6		
			1	2	
		−	1	2	
				0	

1. Divide the first digit by the divisor, 4. Ask: *How many 4s in 2?* There are **no** 4s in 2, so write 0 above the line.

2. Point to the 0 and **multiply** it by the divisor. $0 \times 4 = 0$. Write the answer 0 below and **subtract** it. $2 - 0 = 2$

3. Bring down the next digit to give 29. Ask: *How many 4s in 29?* Write the whole number part of the answer, 7, above.

4. Point to the digit just written (7) and **multiply** it by the divisor. $7 \times 4 = 28$. Write the answer, 28, under the 29. Draw a line under it and **subtract** it. $29 - 28 = 1$

5. Keep going, bringing down the next digit and dividing by the divisor, 4, each time. Write the whole number part of the answer above, then multiply it by the divisor and subtract. If you get zero at the end there is no remainder.

Now you try

1

	0	3	5	7	r1
5)	1	7	8	6	
−	0				
	1	7			
−	1	5			
		2	8		
	−	2	5		
			3	6	
		−	3	5	
				1	

2

	0	9	6	6	
3)	2	8	9	8	
−	0				
	2	8			
−	2	7			
		1	9		
	−	1	8		
			1	8	
		−	1	8	
				0	

More practice

Set out these questions yourself to answer them.

3 $3759 \div 4 = ?$

		0	9	3	9	r3
4	)	3	7	5	9	
−		0				
		3	7			
−		3	6			
			1	5		
	−		1	2		
				3	9	
		−		3	6	
					3	

4 $5894 \div 6 = ?$

		0	9	8	2	r2
6	)	5	8	9	4	
−		0				
		5	8			
−		5	4			
			4	9		
	−		4	8		
				1	4	
		−		1	2	
					2	

Problem solving

Use spare squared paper and long division to solve these problems.

5 Fred won £3725. He gives one-fifth of the amount to charity. How much does he give to charity?

£745

6 How many weeks is 2219 days?

317 weeks

7 Darshna says that 456 × 3 is 1368. Use long division to show if she is correct.

Yes, she is correct.

8 How many rows of nine chairs can be made with 7362 chairs?

818

How did I find Step 5? ☐ Easy ☐ OK ☐ Difficult

Step 6: Four-digit ÷ one-digit long division, answers with zeros

Questions that have zeros in the answer can sometimes be trickier. Just work through them in the same way and remember that zero multiplied by any number is zero.

What to do

$3625 \div 4 = ?$

	Th	H	T	U	
	0	9	0	6	rl
4)	3	6	2	5	
−	0				
	3	6			
−	3	6			
		0	2		
−			0		
			2	5	
−			2	4	
				1	

1 Divide the first digit by the divisor, 4. Ask: *How many 4s in 3?* There are **no** 4s in 3, so write 0 above.

2 Point to the 0 and **multiply** it by the divisor. $0 \times 4 = 0$. Write the answer 0 below and **subtract** it. $3 - 0 = 3$

3 Bring down the next digit to give 36. Ask: *How many 4s in 36?* Write the answer, 9, above. Point to the digit just written (9) and **multiply** it by the divisor. $9 \times 4 = 36$. Write the answer, 36, and subtract it from 36 to give 0.

4 Bring down the next digit, 2. Ask: *How many 4s in 2?* There are **no** 4s in 2, so write 0 above. Multiply 0 by 4 and write it below. Subtract 0 from 2 to give 2.

5 Bring down the next digit, 5, and complete the calculation.

Now you try

1

	1	2	0	9	rl
5)	6	0	4	6	
−	5				
	1	0			
−	1	0			
		0	4		
−			0		
			4	6	
−			4	5	
				1	

2

	1	4	0	9	
3)	4	2	2	7	
−	3				
	1	2			
−	1	2			
		0	2		
−			0		
			2	7	
−			2	7	
				0	

More practice

Set out these questions yourself to answer them.

3 8296 ÷ 4 = ?

```
        2  0  7  4
   4 ) 8  2  9  6
     - 8
        0  2
     -     0
           2  9
        -  2  8
              1  6
           -  1  6
                 0
```

4 8682 ÷ 7 = ?

```
        1  2  4  0  r2
   7 ) 8  6  8  2
     - 7
        1  6
     -  1  4
           2  8
        -  2  8
              0  2
           -     0
                 2
```

Problem solving

Use spare squared paper and long division to solve these problems.

5 A farmer has 8120 sheep. He takes one-quarter of them to market. How many does he take to market?

2030

6 How many 5p coins would make up 7515p (£75.15)?

1503

7 A number is multiplied by three to give the answer 2721. Use long division to find the number.

907

8 There are six identical crates, each holding exactly the same items. Together they weigh 6504kg. What does each crate weigh?

1084kg

| **How did I find Step 6?** | ☐ Easy | ☐ OK | ☐ Difficult |

Check-up test I Three-, four- and five-digit ÷ one-digit

Steps 1 and 2: use short division

1

```
      1   6   8
  4 ) 6  ²7  ³2
```

2 84696 ÷ 7 = ?

```
        1   2   0   9   9  r3
  7 ) 8  ¹4   6  ⁶9  ⁶6
```

Step 3: use long division

3

```
       2   4  r1
  4 ) 9   7
  -  8
       1   7
  -    1   6
               1
```

4 89 ÷ 3 = ?

```
         2   9  r2
  3 ) 8   9
  -   6
         2   9
  -      2   7
                 2
```

Steps 4 and 5: use long division

5

```
       1   3   7  r2
  5 ) 6   8   7
  -  5
       1   8
  -    1   5
                3   7
  -             3   5
                        2
```

6 3759 ÷ 4 = ?

```
         0   9   3   9  r3
  4 ) 3   7   5   9
  -  0
         3   7
  -      3   6
                 1   5
  -             1   2
                        3   9
  -                     3   6
                                3
```

Step 6: use long division

7

```
        1   4   0   9
   3 ) 4   2   2   7
     - 3
         1   2
       - 1   2
             0   2
           -     0
                 2   7
               - 2   7
                     0
```

8

```
        0   4   0   5
   7 ) 2   8   3   5
     - 0
         2   8
       - 2   8
             0   3
           -     0
                 3   5
               - 3   5
                     0
```

Steps 3 to 6 mixed: use long division

Use spare squared paper for working.

9 How many rows of nine bricks can be made with 154 bricks, and how many bricks will be left over?

17 rows with 1 left over

10 If 189 children get into groups of seven, how many groups are there?   27

11 There are 3756 tyres in a car factory. How many four-wheeled cars can be fitted with a set of tyres?   939

7 ☐

8 ☐

9 ☐

10 ☐

11 ☐

Total test score

Score	1	2	3	4	5	6	7	8	9	10	11
%	9	18	27	36	45	55	64	73	82	91	100

11 ☐

Step 7: Three-digit ÷ 11 long division, no zeros in answers

In this step we will use long division for dividing by a two-digit number, 11. We use the same approach as before: **DMS (Divide, Multiply, Subtract)** *then bring down the next digit*.

$685 ÷ 11$

What to do

$685 ÷ 11 = ?$

		H	T	U	
			6		
1	1)	6	8	5	
	−	6	6		
			2		

1 To divide by a two-digit number, 11, look at the first two digits of the other number together. Ask: *How many 11s in 68?* The answer is 6, so write 6 above the tens digit.

2 Point to the 6 and multiply it by the divisor. $6 × 11 = 66$. Write the answer, 66, below. Draw a line under it and subtract it. $68 − 66 = 2$

3 Bring down the next digit to give 25. Ask: *How many 11s in 25?* There are 2, so write 2 at the top.

4 Point to the digit just written (2) and multiply it by the divisor. $2 × 11 = 22$. Write the answer, 22, under the 25. Draw a line under it and subtract it. $25 − 22 = 3$

5 As there are no more digits to divide, write the remainder 3 at the top to complete the answer.

			6	2	r3
1	1)	6	8	5	
	−	6	6	↓	
			2	5	
		−	2	2	
				3	

Now you try

1

			5	3	r2
1	1)	5	8	5	
	−	5	5	↓	
			3	5	
		−	3	3	
				2	

2

			6	7	r1
1	1)	7	3	8	
	−	6	6		
			7	8	
		−	7	7	
				1	

More practice

Set out these questions yourself to answer them.

3 415 ÷ 11 = ?

```
            3   7  r8
   1  1 ) 4   1   5
      -  3   3
             8   5
        -    7   7
                 8
```

4 285 ÷ 11 = ?

```
            2   5  r10
   1  1 ) 2   8   5
      -  2   2
             6   5
        -    5   5
             1   0
```

5 320 ÷ 11 = ?

```
            2   9  r1
   1  1 ) 3   2   0
      -  2   2
         1   0   0
        -    9   9
                 1
```

6 655 ÷ 11 = ?

```
            5   9  r6
   1  1 ) 6   5   5
      -  5   5
         1   0   5
        -    9   9
                 6
```

Problem solving

Use spare squared paper for working.

7 How many 11s are in 902? _____82_____

8 How many football teams of 11 players can be made with 209 players? _____19_____

9 There are 732 soldiers. How many rows of 11 soldiers can be formed, and how many soldiers will be left over?

66 rows with 6 left over

How did I find Step 7? ☐ Easy ☐ OK ☐ Difficult

Step 8: Four-digit ÷ 11 long division, with zeros in answers

Here we will use long division for dividing four-digit numbers by 11. Watch out for zeros in the answers.

What to do

$4504 \div 11 = ?$

			Th	H	T	U	
				4	0	9	r5
1	1	)	4	5	0	4	
	–		4	4			
				1	0		
	–				0		
				1	0	4	
	–				9	9	
						5	

1 Look at the first two digits of the number being divided. Ask: *How many 11s in 45?* There are 4, so write 4 above the hundreds digit.

2 Point to the 4 and **multiply** it by the divisor. $4 \times 11 = 44$. Write the answer below and **subtract** it. $45 - 44 = 1$

3 Bring down the next digit to give 10. Ask: *How many 11s in 10?* There are **no** 11s in 10, so write 0 at the top.

4 **Multiply** the zero by the divisor. $0 \times 11 = 0$. Write 0 under the 10 and **subtract** it. $10 - 0 = 10$

5 Bring down the next digit to give 104. Ask: *How many 11s in 104?* There are 9. Continue in the same way by subtracting to find the remainder to complete the answer.

Now you try

1

			6	0	9	r9
1	1	)	6	7	0	8
	–	6	6			
			1	0		
		–		0		
			1	0	8	
		–		9	9	
					9	

2

			3	0	5	r1
1	1	)	3	3	5	6
	–	3	3			
			0	5		
		–		0		
			5	6		
		–	5	5		
				1		

More practice   Set out these questions yourself to answer them.

3 8904 ÷ 11 = ?

```
          8  0  9 │r5
   1 1 ) 8  9  0  4
     -  8  8
           1  0
        -     0
           1  0  4
        -     9  9
                 5
```

4 7781 ÷ 11 = ?

```
          7  0  7 │r4
   1 1 ) 7  7  8  1
     -  7  7
           0  8
        -     0
              8  1
           -  7  7
                 4
```

5 9963 ÷ 11 = ?

```
          9  0  5 │r8
   1 1 ) 9  9  6  3
     -  9  9
           0  6
        -     0
              6  3
           -  5  5
                 8
```

6 5600 ÷ 11 = ?

```
          5  0  9 │r1
   1 1 ) 5  6  0  0
     -  5  5
           1  0
        -     0
              1  0  0
           -     9  9
                    1
```

Problem solving   Use spare squared paper for working.

7 Make as many four-digit numbers as you can using the digits 3, 0, 3, 2. Divide each of them by 11. What different answers can you make?

3320→301 r9, 3302→300 r2, 3230→293 r7, 3203→291 r2,

3032→275 r7, 3023→274 r9, 2330→211 r9,

2303→209 r4, 2033→184 r9

How did I find Step 8?   ☐ Easy   ☐ OK   ☐ Difficult

Step 9: Four-digit ÷ 12 long division

Now let's try using long division to divide by 12. For long division it is sometimes useful to write out the multiples of the divisor. Here are the first ten multiples of 12.

1	12
2	24
3	36
4	48
5	60
6	72
7	84
8	96
9	108
10	120

What to do

$4554 \div 12 = ?$

		Th	H	T	U	
			3	7	9	r6
1	2)	4	5	5	4	
	−		3	6		
				9	5	
		−		8	4	
				1	1	4
		−		1	0	8
						6

1 Look at the first two digits of the number being divided. Ask: *How many 12s in 45?* Use your list of multiples to help you. You can see that 3 lots of 12 is 36, so write 3 above the hundreds digit and 36 underneath the 45. Then subtract it. 45 − 36 = 9

2 Bring down the next digit to give 95. Ask: *How many 12s in 95?* As 7 lots of 12 is 84, write 7 above and 84 below. Subtract it. 95 − 84 = 11

3 Bring down the next digit to give 114. Ask: *How many 12s in 114?* As 9 lots of 12 is 108, write 9 above and 108 below. Subtract to find the remainder to complete the answer.

Now you try

1

			6	1	5	r8
1	2)	7	3	8	8	
	−	7	2			
			1	8		
		−	1	2		
				6	8	
			−	6	0	
					8	

2

			4	2	1	r4
1	2)	5	0	5	6	
	−	4	8			
			2	5		
		−	2	4		
				1	6	
			−	1	2	
					4	

More practice Set out these questions yourself to answer them.

3 8997 ÷ 12 = ?

```
          7  4  9  r9
   1  2 ) 8  9  9  7
       -  8  4
             5  9
          -  4  8
                1  1  7
             -  1  0  8
                      9
```

4 3816 ÷ 12 = ?

```
          3  1  8
   1  2 ) 3  8  1  6
       -  3  6
             2  1
          -  1  2
                9  6
             -  9  6
                   0
```

5 9963 ÷ 12 = ?

```
          8  3  0  r3
   1  2 ) 9  9  6  3
       -  9  6
             3  6
          -  3  6
                0  3
             -     0
                   3
```

6 6767 ÷ 12 = ?

```
          5  6  3  r11
   1  2 ) 6  7  6  7
       -  6  0
             7  6
          -  7  2
                4  7
             -  3  6
                1  1
```

Problem solving Use spare squared paper for working.

7 Make as many four-digit numbers as you can using the digits 7, 7, 3, 7. Divide each of them by 12. What do you notice about each of the answers?

7773→647 r9, 7737→644 r9, 7377→614 r9, 3777→314 r9.

They all have a remainder of 9.

How did I find Step 9? ☐ Easy ☐ OK ☐ Difficult

Step 10: Four-digit ÷ 13 long division

As we move on to dividing by larger numbers such as 13, you will begin to see how important it is to be able to work out the multiples of the divisor. Here are the first ten multiples of 13. They can be found using your knowledge of the 10 and the 3 times tables: $7 \times 3 = 21$ and $7 \times 10 = 70$, so $7 \times 13 = 91$.

1	13
2	26
3	39
4	52
5	65
6	78
7	91
8	104
9	117
10	130

What to do

$6499 \div 13 = ?$

1   Look at the first two digits of the number being divided. Ask: *How many 13s in 64?* Use the list of multiples to help you. You can see that 4 lots of 13 is 52, so write 4 above the hundreds digit and 52 underneath the 64. Then subtract it. $64 - 52 = 12$

2   Bring down the next digit to give 129. Ask: *How many 13s in 129?* As 9 lots of 13 is 117, write 9 above and 117 below. Subtract it. $129 - 117 = 12$

3   Bring down the next digit to give 129. Ask: *How many 13s in 129?* Again, 9 lots of 13 is 117, so write 9 above and 117 below. Subtract to find the remainder to complete the answer.

		Th	H	T	U	
			4	9	9	r12
1 3	)	6	4	9	9	
	−	5	2			
			1	2	9	
	−		1	1	7	
			•	1	2	9
	−			1	1	7
					1	2

Now you try

1

			5	6	8	r4
1	3)	7	3	8	8	
	−	6	5			
			8	8		
		−	7	8		
			1	0	8	
		−	1	0	4	
					4	

2

			3	9	1	r3
1	3)	5	0	8	6	
	−	3	9			
			1	1	8	
		−	1	1	7	
				1	6	
			−	1	3	
					3	

More practice   Set out these questions yourself to answer them.

3 8997 ÷ 13 = ?

```
              6  9  2  r1
    1  3 ) 8  9  9  7
          - 7  8
             1  1  9
           - 1  1  7
                2  7
              - 2  6
                   1
```

4 5447 ÷ 13 = ?

```
              4  1  9
    1  3 ) 5  4  4  7
          - 5  2
             2  4
           - 1  3
             1  1  7
           - 1  1  7
                0
```

Problem solving

5 Find the error in this calculation and say what the correct answer should be.

Error: The second 8 in the answer should be a 7. And the number subtracted from the second 101 should be 91, with a remainder of 10.

Correct answer: 677 r10

```
                 6  7  8  r3
    1  3 ) 8  8  1  1
          - 7  8
             1  0  1
           -    9  1
             1  0  1
           - 1  0  4
                   3
```

Use spare squared paper for working.

6 How many teams of 13 rugby league players can be made with 1352 players?   104

7 Tickets for a theme park cost £13 each. How many tickets were sold if £5954 was taken at the gate?   458

| **How did I find Step 10?** | ☐ Easy | ☐ OK | ☐ Difficult |

Check-up test 2 Three- and four-digit ÷ 11, 12 or 13

Step 7: use long division

1

```
            4   1  r8
   1  1 ) 4  5  9
      -   4  4
              1  9
          -   1  1
                  8
```

2 $416 ÷ 11 = ?$

```
            3   7  r9
   1  1 ) 4  1  6
      -  3  3
            8  6
         -  7  7
               9
```

Step 8: use long division

3

```
            9  0  5  r10
   1  1 ) 9  9  6  5
      -  9  9
            0  6
         -     0
               6  5
            -  5  5
                  1  0
```

4 $3403 ÷ 11 = ?$

```
            3  0  9  r4
   1  1 ) 3  4  0  3
      -  3  3
            1  0
         -     0
               1  0  3
            -     9  9
                     4
```

Step 9: use long division

5

```
            8  3  0  r3
   1  2 ) 9  9  6  3
      -  9  6
            3  6
         -  3  6
               0  3
            -     0
                  3
```

6 $4255 ÷ 12 = ?$

```
            3  5  4  r7
   1  2 ) 4  2  5  5
      -  3  6
            6  5
         -  6  0
               5  5
            -  4  8
                  7
```

1
2
3
4
5
6

Step 10: use long division

7

```
              5  6  8  r4
   1  3 ) 7   3  8  8
        -  6  5
              8  8
           -  7  8
              1  0  8
           -  1  0  4
                    4
```

8

```
              3  9  1  r3
   1  3 ) 5   0  8  6
        -  3  9
              1  1  8
           -  1  1  7
                 1  6
              -  1  3
                    3
```

1	13
2	26
3	39
4	52
5	65
6	78
7	91
8	104
9	117
10	130

☐ 7
☐ 8

Steps 7 to 10 mixed: use long division

Use spare squared paper for working.

9 How many teams of 13 rugby league players can
be made with 3692 players?

_284_   ☐ 9

10 There are 12 months in a year. How many years
is 1008 months?

84 years   ☐ 10

11 A lottery prize is won by a group of 11 people.
They share £9537 equally between them.
How much does each get?

_£867_   ☐ 11

12 As 12 inches are equal in length to 1 foot, how many
feet is 4452 inches?

371 feet   ☐ 12

Total test score

☐ 12

Score	1	2	3	4	5	6	7	8	9	10	11	12
%	8	17	25	33	42	50	58	67	75	83	92	100

Step 11: Four-digit ÷ 14, 15 or 16 long division

You can write the first ten multiples of 14, 15 and 16 to help you with the divisions in this step. Complete these lists.

Then divide in the same way as before, using the multiples in the appropriate list to help you.

1	14
2	28
3	42
4	56
5	70
6	84
7	98
8	112
9	126
10	140

1	15
2	30
3	45
4	60
5	75
6	90
7	105
8	120
9	135
10	150

1	16
2	32
3	48
4	64
5	80
6	96
7	112
8	128
9	144
10	160

Now you try

1

```
            7 0 9 r4
  1 4 ) 9 9 3 0
      - 9 8
          1 3
        -   0
          1 3 0
        - 1 2 6
              4
```

2

```
          5 3 3 r1
  1 5 ) 7 9 9 6
      - 7 5
          4 9
        - 4 5
            4 6
          - 4 5
                1
```

3

```
          4 5 9
  1 6 ) 7 3 4 4
      - 6 4
          9 4
        - 8 0
          1 4 4
        - 1 4 4
              0
```

4

```
          2 8 4 r10
  1 4 ) 3 9 8 6
      - 2 8
          1 1 8
        - 1 1 2
              6 6
            - 5 6
              1 0
```

More practice

Try these without the grids.

5
```
            1  8  0  r14
    1  6 ) 2  8  9  4
         - 1  6
           ──────
           1  2  9
         - 1  2  8
           ──────
                 1  4
               -    0
               ──────
                 1  4
```

6
```
                 5  2  6  r13
    1  5 ) 7  9  0  3
         - 7  5
           ──────
              4  0
            - 3  0
              ──────
              1  0  3
            -    9  0
              ──────
                 1  3
```

Problem solving

Use spare squared paper for working.

7 With imperial units of mass, 14 pounds equals 1 stone.
How many stone is 1540 pounds?

110 stone

8 With imperial units of mass, 16 ounces equals 1 pound.
How many pounds is 3424 ounces?

214 pounds

9 A factory makes ribbon and cuts it into equal lengths.
A length of ribbon that is 1755m long is cut into 15 equal lengths.
How long is each length?

_117m_

10 14 people share £4858 equally between them. How much
does each get?

_£347_

11 How many £15 donations did a charity receive if £6990
in total was donated?

_466_

| **How did I find Step 11?** | ☐ Easy | ☐ OK | ☐ Difficult |

Step 12: Four-digit ÷ 17, 18 or 19 long division, where the first two digits are smaller than the divisor

Complete the first ten multiples of 17, 18 and 19 to help you with the divisions in this step.

In this step you'll find out what to do if the first two digits form a number that is smaller than the divisor, such as 1592 ÷ 17 where 15 is smaller than 17.

1	17
2	34
3	51
4	68
5	85
6	102
7	119
8	136
9	153
10	170

1	18
2	36
3	54
4	72
5	90
6	108
7	126
8	144
9	162
10	180

1	19
2	38
3	57
4	76
5	95
6	114
7	133
8	152
9	171
10	190

What to do

1592 ÷ 17 = ?

1 Look at the first two digits of the number being divided. Here they form the number 15. If this is less than the divisor, which is 17 here, look instead at the first **three** digits together. Ask: How many 17s in 159? Use your list of multiples to help you. You can see that 9 lots of 17 is 153, so write 9 above the tens digit and 153 underneath the 159. Then subtract it. 159 – 153 = 6

2 Bring down the next digit to give 62. Ask: How many 17s in 62? As 3 lots of 17 is 51, write 3 above and 51 below. Subtract to find the remainder to complete the answer.

```
         Th  H   T   U
                 9   3  r11
  1  7 ) 1   5   9   2
       - 1   5   3
                 6   2
               - 5   1
                 1   1
```

Now you try

1
```
              6  6
 1  7 ) 1  1  2  2
      - 1  0  2
           1  0  2
         - 1  0  2
                 0
```

2
```
              7  4  r10
 1  8 ) 1  3  4  2
      - 1  2  6
            8  2
          - 7  2
             1  0
```

More practice

3

```
            8  7 │ r9
 1  9 ) 1  6  6  2
      - 1  5  2
            1  4  2
          - 1  3  3
                  9
```

4

```
            7  9 │ r16
 1  7 ) 1  3  5  9
      - 1  1  9
            1  6  9
          - 1  5  3
               1  6
```

Try these without the grids.

5

```
            6  0  r12
 1  8 ) 1  0  9  2
      - 1  0  8
              1  2
            -    0
              1  2
```

6

```
            7  9  r5
 1  9 ) 1  5  0  6
      - 1  3  3
            1  7  6
          - 1  7  1
                  5
```

Problem solving

Use spare squared paper for working.

7   A swimming pool is being tiled. Each square tile is 18cm wide.
How many will be needed to make a row of tiles 1134cm long?   63

8   Tickets for a concert cost £17 each. How many tickets were sold
if £1513 was taken at the box office?   89

| **How did I find Step 12?** | ☐ Easy | ☐ OK | ☐ Difficult |

Step 13: Four-digit ÷ a number between 11 and 19 long division

What to do

These mixed questions involve dividing by a number between 11 and 19. Use the same strategies as for the previous steps. This time, however, you are not given many multiples. Write the multiples into the list provided for each question as you need them.

Now you try

1

```
          3  3  4  r7
1  3 ) 4  3  4  9
    -  3  9
          4  4
       -  3  9
             5  9
          -  5  2
                7
```

1	13
2	___
3	39
4	52
5	___
6	___
7	___
8	___
9	___
10	___

2

```
             2  3  5  r1
1  7 ) 3  9  9  6
    -  3  4
          5  9
       -  5  1
             8  6
          -  8  5
                1
```

1	17
2	34
3	51
4	___
5	85
6	___
7	___
8	___
9	___
10	___

3

```
          5  1  7  r7
1  9 ) 9  8  3  0
    -  9  5
          3  3
       -  1  9
             1  4  0
          -  1  3  3
                   7
```

1	19
2	___
3	___
4	___
5	95
6	___
7	133
8	___
9	___
10	___

4

```
             8  8  r6
1  4 ) 1  2  3  8
    -  1  1  2
          1  1  8
       -  1  1  2
                6
```

1	14
2	___
3	___
4	___
5	___
6	___
7	___
8	112
9	___
10	___

More practice

Try these without the grids. Make your own notes to work out any multiples you need.

5
```
              8  9  1  r3
         _____
    1  1 ) 9  8  0  4
       -  8  8
         _____
            1  0  0
         -     9  9
            _____
                  1  4
              -   1  1
                _____
                      3
```

6
```
              4  0  9  r5
         _____
    1  2 ) 4  9  1  3
       -  4  8
         _____
            1  1
         -        0
            _____
               1  1  3
            -  1  0  8
              _____
                     5
```

Problem solving

Use spare paper for working.

7   How many years is 4128 months?   <u>344 years</u>

8   With imperial units of mass, 16 ounces equals 1 pound. How many pounds is 6992 ounces?   <u>437 pounds</u>

9   A number is multiplied by 13 to give the answer 3549. Use long division to find the number.   <u>273</u>

10   15 people together win a prize. They share £1335 equally between them. How much does each get?   <u>£89</u>

11   The restaurant bill for a party of 17 people is £1292. They agree to share the bill equally between them. How much does each person pay?   <u>£76</u>

How did I find Step 13?   ☐ Easy   ☐ OK   ☐ Difficult

Step 14: Four-digit ÷ a number between 11 and 19
long division, with fraction remainders

Sometimes when we divide, giving an answer with a remainder doesn't make sense. For example: *Pour 3685ml of water into 13 jars so that there is the same amount in each jar.* Having some water left over isn't an option. So your answer can't just have a remainder.

3685ml ÷ 13

What to do

$3685 \div 13 = ?$

1   Divide as before and work out what the remainder will be. Here $3685 \div 13 = 283$ r6.

2   We can't give the answer with a remainder of 6. Dividing the remainder 6 by the divisor 13 gives you the fraction $\frac{6}{13}$.

3   See that the numerator of the fraction (the number on the top) is the remainder and the denominator (the number on the bottom) is the divisor. So the answer to the division is $283\frac{6}{13}$.

		Th	H	T	U	
			2	8	3	$\frac{6}{13}$
1	3)	3	6	8	5	
	−	2	6			
		1	0	8		
	−	1	0	4		
				4	5	
		−		3	9	
					6	

$$3685 \div 3 = 283\frac{6}{13}$$

Now you try

Give remainders as fractions.

1

			2	0	6	$\frac{5}{19}$
1	9)	3	9	1	9	
	−	3	8			
			1	1		
		−		0		
			1	1	9	
		−	1	1	4	
					5	

2

			4	1	7	$\frac{13}{16}$
1	6)	6	6	8	5	
	−	6	4			
			2	8		
		−	1	6		
			1	2	5	
		−	1	1	2	
				1	3	

More practice

Give remainders as fractions.

3

```
            6  1  4  8/15
   1  5 ) 9  2  1  8
       -  9  0
             2  1
          -  1  5
                6  8
             -  6  0
                   8
```

4

```
               9  1  3/14
   1  4 ) 1  2  7  7
       -  1  2  6
                1  7
             -  1  4
                   3
```

Problem solving

Give each answer with the remainder as a fraction. Use spare paper for working.

5   A school playground has a length of 2754cm. A teacher wants to split the length into 12 equal sections. How long would each section be?

$229\frac{1}{2}$cm or $229\frac{6}{12}$cm

6   With imperial units of mass, 14 pounds equals 1 stone. How many stone is 1183 pounds?

$84\frac{1}{2}$ or $84\frac{7}{14}$ stone

7   Work out the missing digits in this calculation.

$273\boxed{1} \div 13 = 210\boxed{\tfrac{1}{13}}$

How did I find Step 14?   ☐ Easy   ☐ OK   ☐ Difficult

Check-up test 3 Four-digit ÷ a number between 11 and 19, including fraction remainders

Steps 11, 12 and 13

Give answers with remainders for these.

Complete the lists of multiples when needed.

1 9965 ÷ 15 = ?

```
              6  6  4  r5
    1  5 ) 9  9  6  5
       -  9  0
             9  6
          -  9  0
                6  5
             -  6  0
                   5
```

1	15
2	30
3	__
4	60
5	__
6	90
7	__
8	120
9	__
10	__

2 1242 ÷ 15 = ?

```
                 8  2  rl2
    1  5 ) 1  2  4  2
       -  1  2  0
                4  2
             -  3  0
                1  2
```

3

```
           5  1  7  r7
  1  9 ) 9  8  3  0
     -  9  5
           3  3
        -  1  9
           1  4  0
        -  1  3  3
                 7
```

1	19
2	__
3	__
4	__
5	95
6	114
7	133
8	152
9	__
10	__

4 1302 ÷ 19 = ?

```
                 6  8  rl0
    1  9 ) 1  3  0  2
       -  1  1  4
                1  6  2
             -  1  5  2
                   1  0
```

Step 14

Give remainders as fractions for these.

Complete the lists of multiples when needed.

5

```
          4  1  7  13/16
   1  6) 6  6  8  5
      -  6  4
            2  8
         -  1  6
            1  2  5
         -  1  1  2
               1  3
```

1	16
2	__
3	__
4	64
5	__
6	__
7	112
8	__
9	144
10	__

6

```
             7  9  13/16
   1  6) 1  2  7  7
      -  1  1  2
            1  5  7
         -  1  4  4
               1  3
```

☐ 5
☐ 6

Steps 11 to 14 mixed

Use spare paper for working.

7 All the rows in a stadium have 18 seats. How many rows are there if there are 2106 seats?

117

☐ 7

8 14 pounds equals 1 stone. How many stone is 1169 pounds? Give any remainder as a fraction of a stone.

$83\frac{1}{2}$ or $83\frac{7}{14}$ stone

☐ 8

9 Share £9536 equally between 16 people. How much does each get?

£596

☐ 9

10 Jon worked for 17 days. He was paid the same amount each day. He earned a total of £816. What was his daily rate?

£48

☐ 10

Total test score

Score	1	2	3	4	5	6	7	8	9	10
%	10	20	30	40	50	60	70	80	90	100

___
10

Step 15: Four-digit ÷ a number in the 20s
long division

Now that you can do the long division method for numbers to 19, we can try dividing by numbers in their 20s.

$5322 \div 23 = ?$

What to do

1 Ask: *How many 23s in 53?* Write 2 above and multiply 2 by 23 to give 46 below. Subtract it. 53 – 46 = 7

2 Bring down the next digit to give 72. Ask: *How many 23s in 72?* Write 3 above and multiply 3 by 23 to give 69 below. Subtract it. 72 – 69 = 3

3 Bring down the next digit to give 32. Ask: *How many 23s in 32?* Write 1 above and 23 below. Subtract it. 32 – 23 = 9

4 Share 9 between the divisor, 23, to give the fraction $\frac{9}{23}$ to complete the answer.

		Th	H	T	U	
			2	3	1	$\frac{9}{23}$
2	3)	5	3	2	2	
	–	4	6			
			7	2		
		–	6	9		
				3	2	
			–	2	3	
					9	

$5322 \div 23 = 231 \frac{9}{23}$

Now you try

Write the multiples into the list provided for each question if you need to.

Continue to give remainders as fractions here.

1

			3	1	5	$\frac{19}{22}$
2	2)	6	9	4	9	
	–	6	6			
			3	4		
		–	2	2		
			1	2	9	
		–	1	1	0	
				1	9	

1	22
2	___
3	66
4	___
5	110
6	___
7	___
8	___
9	___
10	___

2

			5	4	$\frac{1}{24}$
2	4)	1	2	9	7
	–	1	2	0	
			9	7	
		–	9	6	
				1	

1	24
2	48
3	___
4	96
5	120
6	___
7	___
8	___
9	___
10	___

More practice   Set out these questions yourself to answer them.

Give remainders as fractions.

3 5275 ÷ 21 = ?

```
              2  5  1   4/21
  2  1 ) 5  2  7  5
     -  4  2
           1  0  7
        -  1  0  5
                 2  5
              -  2  1
                    4
```

1	21
2	42
3	___
4	___
5	105
6	___
7	___
8	___
9	___
10	___

4 2209 ÷ 26 = ?

```
                 8  4   25/26
  2  6 ) 2  2  0  9
      -  2  0  8
              1  2  9
           -  1  0  4
                 2  5
```

1	26
2	___
3	___
4	104
5	___
6	___
7	___
8	208
9	___
10	___

Problem solving

Use spare paper for working.

5 Answer these questions using long division.

5420 ÷ 25   1357 ÷ 23   3429 ÷ 27   2943 ÷ 29

$216\frac{20}{25}$ or $216\frac{4}{5}$ 59   127 $101\frac{14}{29}$

6 There are 24 hours in a day. How many days is 8760 hours?   365 days

7 On average Paulo's car travels 28 miles for each gallon of petrol. How many gallons of petrol has he used if he has travelled 4732 miles this year?   169 gallons

How did I find Step 15?   ☐ Easy   ☐ OK   ☐ Difficult

Step 16: Four-digit ÷ two-digit long division

This step involves dividing by any two-digit number. Continue to give remainders as fractions. Be careful not to get your carrying numbers mixed up.

What to do

$3512 \div 67 = ?$

1 The first two digits of the number, 35, are smaller than the divisor (67), so look at the first **three** digits. Ask: *How many 67s in 351?* Estimate how many you think there are by approximating: $70 \times 5 = 350$, so try 5.

		Th	H	T	U	
				5		
6	7)	3	5	1	2	
	−	3	3₃	5		

2 Write 5 above the tens digit and multiply 5 by 67. Use written multiplication to do this. $5 \times 7 = 35$, write 5 and carry 3. Then do 5×6 tens $= 30$ tens plus the 3 tens you have carried to give 33 tens.

3 Use written subtraction, exchanging if you need to: $351 - 335 = 16$. Bring down the next digit to give 162. Ask: *How many 67s in 162?* Make an estimate, for example 2, and write it above.

4 Use written multiplication to find $2 \times 67 = 134$. Then use written subtraction: $162 - 134 = 28$.

5 Then write the remainder as a fraction $\frac{28}{67}$.

				5	2	$\frac{28}{67}$
6	7)	3	⁴5	¹1	2	
	−	3	3₃	5		
			1	⁵6	¹2	
		−	1	3₁	4	
				2	8	

Now you try

1

				4	8	$\frac{1}{36}$
3	6)	1	⁶7	¹2	9	
	−	1	4₂	4		
			2	8	9	
		−	2	8₄	8	
					1	

2

				8	3	$\frac{21}{58}$
5	8)	4	⁷8	¹3	5	
	−	4	6₆	4		
			1	9	5	
		−	1	7₂	4	
				2	1	

More practice

3

```
                6   3   17/46
    4  6 ) 2  ⁸9¹ 1   5
       -  2   7₃ 6
              1 ⁴5¹ 5
           -  1  3₁ 8
                 1   7
```

4

```
                5   3   36/73
    7  3 ) 3  ⁸9¹ 0   5
       -  3   6₁ 5
              2 ⁴5¹ 5
           -  2  1   9
                 3   6
```

5

```
                4   4   55/84
    8  4 ) 3  ⁶7¹ 5   1
       -  3   3₁ 6
              3 ⁸9¹ 1
           -  3  3₁ 6
                 5   5
```

6

```
                9   4   56/79
    7  9 ) 7   4   8   2
       -  7   1₈ 1
              3 ⁶7¹ 2
           -  3  1₃ 6
                 5   6
```

Problem solving

Use spare paper for working.

7   A factory has 3864 cartons of juice and puts 92 cartons into each box. How many boxes are needed?   42

8   As part of a school sponsored walk 63 children raised money for a good cause. If £1323 is raised in total, what is the average amount that each child raised?   £21.00

How did I find Step 16?   ☐ Easy   ☐ OK   ☐ Difficult

Step 17: Three-digit ÷ two-digit long division, decimal answers 1 dp

From short division you may remember that remainders can be given as decimals. The same is true for long division. We use a decimal point and extra zero digits. Remember that 552 is the same as 552.0 or 552.00.

What to do

$552 \div 48 = ?$

1 When you reach the end and would normally write a remainder, keep going.

2 Put a decimal point at the end of the number being divided and another above it in the answer.

3 Then put a zero digit to the right of the number and bring it down as the next digit. Here 24 becomes 240. Continue dividing in the same way until you get the remainder zero.

	H	T	U	.	t
			1	1 .	5
4 8)	5	5	2 .	0
	–	4	8		
		7	2		
		–	4	8	↓
			2	4	0
			–	2	4₄	0
					0

Now you try

1

```
          2 3 . 2
  3 5 ) 8 1 2 . 0
      – 7 0
        1 1 2
      – 1 0 ₁5  ↓
            7 0
          – 7 ₁0
              0
```

2

```
          3 2 . 5
  2 6 ) ⁷8 ¹4 5 . 0
      – 7 ₁8
          6 5
        – 5 2  ↓
          1 3 0
        – 1 3 ₃0
              0
```

More practice

3 924 ÷ 56 = ?

```
            1   6 . 5
 5  6 )⁸9ᶜ1 2   4 . 0
     -  5   6
        3 ⁵6ᶜ1 4
     -  3   3 ₃ 6
            2   8   0
         -  2   8 ₃ 0
                    0
```

4 949 ÷ 65 = ?

```
            1   4 . 6
 6  5 )⁸9ᶜ1 4   9 . 0
     -  6   5
        2   9   9
     -  2   6 ₂ 0
            3   9   0
         -  3   9 ₃ 0
                    0
```

Problem solving

Use spare paper for working.

5 There are 28 days in February. Kim earned £714 in February. How much is that on average each day?

£25.50

6 On average Priya's car travels 45 miles for each gallon of diesel. How many gallons of diesel has she used if she has travelled 612 miles this month?

13.6 gallons

7 There are 35 children in the class. The children raise £868 for charity. How much is that on average per child?

£24.80

8 427 ÷ 35 = 12.2
True or false?

true

9 567 ÷ 42 = 14.5
True or false?

false

| How did I find Step 17? | ☐ Easy | ☐ OK | ☐ Difficult |

Step 18: Three-digit ÷ two-digit long division, decimal answers 2 dp

The questions in this final step involve decimal answers that have two digits after the decimal point. Work in the same way and bring down a second zero digit.

What to do

$333 \div 36 = ?$

1 When you reach the end and would normally write a remainder, keep going.

2 Put a decimal point at the end of the number being divided and another above it in the answer.

3 Then put a zero digit to the right of the number and bring it down as the next digit. Here 9 becomes 90.

4 Continue dividing in the same way and bring down the next zero digit so that 18 becomes 180. Your answer is complete when you get the remainder zero.

Now you try

1

2

More practice

Set out these questions yourself to answer them.

3 $319 \div 44 = ?$

				7 .	2	5
4	4	) 3	1	9 . 0	0	
	−	3	0 $_2$	8		
			^{0}1	^{10}1 ^{1}0		
		−		8	8	
				2	2	0
		−		2	2 $_2$ 0	
						0

4 $342 \div 72 = ?$

				4 .	7	5
7	2	) ^{2}3	^{13}4	^{1}2 . 0	0	
	−	2	8	8		
			5	^{3}4 ^{1}0		
		−	5	0 $_1$	4	
				3	6	0
		−		3	6 $_1$ 0	
						0

Problem solving

Use spare paper for working.

5 Which **three** of these answers are correct answers to the question $156 \div 48$? Circle them.

(3 r12) $3\frac{1}{2}$ 3.5 (3.25) 3.75 (3$\frac{12}{48}$)

6 There are 28 days in February. Conrad collected £133 of sponsorship money in February. How much is that on average each day?

£4.75

7 A length of wood that is 222cm long is cut into 24 equal lengths. How long is each piece in centimetres?

9.25cm

8 A bonus of £2772 is shared equally between 48 employees. How much does each get?

£57.75

How did I find Step 18? ☐ Easy ☐ OK ☐ Difficult

Final test Three- and four-digit ÷ two-digit including decimal answers

Steps 15 and 16

Give remainders as fractions for these. Complete the list of multiples as needed.

1

$$
22 \overline{\smash{)}\, 9161} \quad 416\tfrac{9}{22}
$$

			4	1	6	$\tfrac{9}{22}$
2	2	)	9	1	6	1
	−	8	8			
			3	6		
		−	2	2		
			1	4	1	
		−	1	3	2	
					9	

1	22
2	___
3	___
4	88
5	___
6	132
7	___
8	___
9	___
10	___

2 $3905 ÷ 73 = ?$

				5	3	$\tfrac{36}{73}$
7	3	)	3 ⁸9 ¹0	5		
	−	3	6 ₁5			
			2 ⁴5 ¹5			
		−	2	1	9	
				3	6	

☐ 1
☐ 2

Steps 17 and 18

Give remainders as decimals for these.

3

			1	4	.	6
6	5	)	⁸9 ¹4	9	.	0
	−	6	5			
		2	9	9		
		−	2	6 ₂	0	
			3	9	0	
		−	3	9 ₃	0	
					0	

4 $323 ÷ 76 = ?$

				4	.	2	5
7	6	)	3	¹2 ¹3	.	0	0
	−	3	0 ₂	4			
		1	⁸9 ¹0				
		−	1	5 ₁	2		
			3	8	0		
		−	3	8 ₃	0		
					0		

☐ 3
☐ 4

Steps 1 to 18 mixed

5

```
            7   4
      ┌──────────
1  1  )  8   1   4
    -  7   7
          ─────
          4   4
      -   4   4
          ─────
              0
```

6

```
            4   1  r8
      ┌──────────
1  1  )  4   5   9
    -  4   4
          ─────
              1   9
          -   1   1
              ─────
                  8
```

□ 5
□ 6

Use spare paper for working.

7 There are 12 months in a year. How many years is 876 months?

73 years □ 7

8 There are 24 hours in a day. How many days is 2112 hours?

88 days □ 8

9 Each row in a theatre has 36 seats. How many rows are there if there are 1152 seats?

_32_ □ 9

10 16 ounces equals 1 pound. How many pounds is 1160 ounces? Give any remainder as a fraction of a pound.

$72\frac{1}{2}$ or $72\frac{8}{16}$ pounds □ 10

11 A length of rope that is 300cm long is cut into 24 equal lengths. How long is each piece in centimetres?

_12.5cm_ □ 11

12 Tickets for a theme park cost £11 each. How many tickets were sold if £5038 was taken at the gate?

_458_ □ 12

13 There are 28 days in February. Li earned £105 by doing jobs in February at home. How much is that on average each day?

_£3.75_ □ 13

14 On average Hannah's car travels 29 miles for each gallon of petrol. How many gallons of petrol has she used if she has travelled 3625 miles this year?

125 gallons □ 14

Total test score

□ 14

Score	1	2	3	4	5	6	7	8	9	10	11	12	13	14
%	7	14	21	29	36	43	50	57	64	71	79	86	93	100

Written Calculation

Group record sheet

Pupil Book: _____

Class/Set: _____

Pupil's name	Check-up test 1	Check-up test 2	Check-up test 3	Final test	Assessment test 1*	Assessment test 2*	Mixed calculations test*

*Available as assessment resources in the back of the **Written Calculation: Teacher's Guide** (ISBN 978 07217 1278 9)